GW00835950

Gallery Books
Editor Peter Fallon
PALE SISTER

Colm Tóibín

PALE SISTER

Gallery Books

Pale Sister
was first published
simultaneously in paperback
and in a clothbound edition
in October 2019.
Reprinted 2021.

The Gallery Press
Loughcrew
Oldcastle
County Meath
Ireland

www.gallerypress.com

ISBN 978 1 91133 778 2

A CIP catalogue record for this book
is available from the British Library.

Pale Sister receives financial assistance
from the Arts Council.

PALE SISTER

Pale Sister was first produced by Audible and the Gate Theatre and had its World Première onstage at the Gate Theatre, Dublin, on 31 October 2019.

ISMENE   *Lisa Dwan*

Director   Carey Perloff
Set and Costume Designer   Jamie Vartan
Lighting Designer   James F Ingalls
Sound Designer   Sinéad Diskin
Associate Director   Davey Kelleher

for Eileen Ahearn

1

In the hour before dawn my sister comes into this room.

Hunted, wounded, she shivers. Her movements darting, then slow and furtive.

There is not a sound.

I do not know if I am afraid.

She turns, her eyes like words. Her gaze pierces the air like a howl.

This is the room where she slept before they found her and took her away.

Silence weighs heavy now like a cave whose mouth has been closed up with stones and clay.

My sister is looking for an opening so that she can find light and cry out. But there is no weak place among the stones; there is no opening.

All the time that she is here she keeps her hands covered.

Let me see! Don't pull them away!

My sister's fingers have been bitten, they have been chewed at, they have been gnawed away by her very own teeth. I see the rawness, the flesh purple and strangely white, the dark, caked blood on the stumps, the teeth marks.

And she smiles at me, she is proud, proud that she has not been idle.

She will now face the morning light, unflinching, clear-eyed, knowing that she, when it mattered, made a difference in the world.

She will persist.

But there will come a time when she will be only a memory, a name. Soon there will be no one left in the world who will have heard her voice.

All the others are dead, except one who lies in a darkened room.

I alone can speak, I alone, the pale sister. The witness.

My sister wants me to walk towards the palace and stand in the sunlight staring.

She wants me to accuse the King with my silence.

Stand and accuse. Stare at him!

She will speak about what must be done. What I must do. How I must remain still and gaze at Creon, and the gaze must be filled with calm accusation.

Standing will be enough. Do not move! Just stand. Stand!

He will be alone with his fear, and there will be many there to see how afraid he is by day as much as by night, how he flinches at a smallest sound.

But he fears silence more than sound.

Outside, in the streets, even by day, no one makes a sound. We live in a time of silence.

Stand and gaze, that is all I ask, pale sister!

I lift the lamp towards her and blind her with its rays.

And then she is gone, gone to lurk in the shadows until the first rays of light appear to frighten her away.

But she will come back.

She leaves the air in this room disturbed as though the light itself is infused with her.

Nothing will settle until she does.

And I do not know when that will be.

But she will speak again. Not about her suffering. Or her fear. Or what she did when he threatened her. She will not speak of how foolish she was, or how impetuous, or how brave. Or how right she was.

Yes, maybe that too.

I wake and dream and wake again. In my sleep I am moving towards land, being pushed forward as each wave breaks and then pulled out again until I struggle not to drown.

And then I am in life again. It is morning in this room.

I have been saved. I am the timid one who wants only quietness. I am like the waters on a calm day that come and go and make only a faint and comforting sound. A sound that makes no one afraid.

But when I fade, so will the truth.

And so I speak. That is why I speak.

I live in the strangeness that comes after.

I am grateful for it, as we all are for the thin sun in the morning sky before it becomes fierce and we move indoors away from its hot grip.

We wait again for twilight, for the softening that returns, as the birds dart through the air, feasting on the flies that have grown lazy now, less vigilant.

I am not less vigilant. Too much has happened for that.

I do not know what my sister was.

But I know what she did and what she said. I am alone in knowing that.

I will say what I know.

I will name who was there.

I will name Eteocles and Polyneices, our two brothers.

I will name my sister Antigone who moved between them in the time they had power.

This was her realm, the place of guile and treachery, of plots and of webbed conspiracy. Eteocles held the reins. Polyneices waited for his turn. Between them was dark suspicion, their followers hungry for spoils.

Whisper to me now as you once whispered of who was most favoured, of what man once banished now returned. The world you walked in was filled with rumours, secrets and spies.

I will not take sides, pale sister. I told you.

Eteocles' men are strutting, gathering their strength.

The men around Polyneices are hungry for power as an animal that is tied when the smell of food is wafting into the air. While the war waged my sister lived in an eternal present. Her arrival here was like a rush of water or wind or sudden rain. She was all movement, breathless with news.

I felt then that I irritated her with my dullness.

They are my brothers and I will not take sides.

As my sister spoke her eyes were filled with the shifting energy of fire.

2

I went to the house of my uncle. Just as my sister became a brother to my two brothers, I became a daughter to my uncle and his wife, and a sister to their son. I sat with my uncle's wife Eurydice, and at the first hint of shadowing night she sent two women to accompany me home.

I wonder if in all the lives that come and go, if there is a special time. If in the lives of birds that fly with such fervour through the early evening sky, or the animals that hunt, or even the trees as they grow strong and firm, or in our own lives, if there is a time that is the golden time, the time when the nest is made, or when the hunting has nourished the lair, or when the tree is bright with fruit, or when we, who are human, live in pure contentment and want only for the day not to darken.

There *was* a day like this, a single golden day before our brothers tore one another apart, a day when I walked freely and alone to my uncle's house, with only a thought for the ease I would find there. In the morning Creon, my uncle, sat with Eurydice his wife and Haemon his son.

I remember Creon's smile, his soft voice, and Haemon gentle too. Some days they did not want to leave us.

I noticed then that Haemon, although he was promised to my sister, would stop and watch me. He would wait until I lifted my eyes to his and then he would lower his eyes.

I would think about his voice, his shy way of glancing to the side, his hesitant smile.

During that time, I got only one single sign of what was to come.

There was an enclosure close to my uncle's house, often used for animals. One morning, as I approached, I saw a terror-stricken youth, barely more than a boy, almost naked, tied to a post, trapped, calling out for help, while two vicious dogs, also tied, barked at him and bared their teeth. They were nearly close enough to touch him. They growled and threatened him and withdrew and sprang towards him again, snarling and yelping. From where I stood I could feel the boy's panic. It would just take one bending of the posts to which the dogs were tied for them to get him and devour him.

My aunt told me that the boy had displeased Creon.

'How long will he be kept there for?'

'Perhaps Creon will take pity on him soon,' she said.

'Where is Creon?'

Eurydice turned away from me. She was trembling. She had already seen what I saw now. Over to the side Creon stood with some men. They were laughing at the boy's distress and egging on the dogs. One man was jumping up in the air with excitement. Creon let out a whoop of encouragement to the dogs and they tried to lunge at the boy who was, by now, so stricken with panic that it was almost impossible to see his face clearly, impossible to see anything other than his desperate efforts to free himself or move sideways away from the dogs as the ropes that bound him dug into his flesh.

'Come away!' Eurydice commanded.

All morning the women moved through the house watch-ful, silent, afraid. Like them I was waiting for a cry, a sign that the dogs had broken free.

'Come to an inner room, so we will not hear.'

When my uncle appeared with Haemon he shrugged and said that the boy had been released. I saw a cloud pass over Creon's face. It was hard, cruel, but flushed as well, almost delighted. It was only when Eurydice approached him with some fruit and some water did he become quiet and contented for a while, like the man I had known before. But there was, and there remained for the rest of that day, an edge to him that was uneasy, guilty, guarded, like someone who will soon be found out.

I saw Creon then. I knew him. As my sister brought home the news of the strife between our brothers, I knew that none of us could trust Creon, whom some believed to be stable, gentle and wise, the man who would be the healer when our brothers attacked each other and they both died.

Out there in the world the story of my sister is known, as though knowledge — knowledge! — were somehow solid, considered, fully reliable, unsullied by man's need, distant from stories and fables and legends. Unsullied by truth.

Truth, yes, truth.

I can hear my sister laugh at the thought of truth.

3

One day when the strife between our brothers had been at its most intense, and I came breathlessly back to the house, afraid to let anyone know what I had been told, I found Antigone there. She was calm, standing away from the door. She was composed. Her voice was even, almost soft.

How much do you know?

They are dead, our brothers are dead.

I had not said these words before. They were like the sound of thunder when the air is purple. They were like blows.

Yes, but only Eteocles is buried. He has left Polyneices to rot under the sun, like a dog, an old hyena.

I know.

Creon has given orders that anyone who touches that body will be buried alive.

I caught her eye in the half-light.

I can implore Creon, I said. I can return to him now. He is . . .

No, stay. Stay here. I do not want you to come with me. Someone must remain.

Since I was with Creon when he heard the news I was ready to tell my sister what I witnessed. I needed her to listen, but she stopped me.

I will bury my brother. I will have to . . .

Creon may change his mind, I said. We can make him change his mind.

No one of ours has ever lain open to the sun. Our brother cannot remain unburied. This does not depend on a man changing his mind.

Later, people came to this house and told me how nervous my sister's gestures were that day, how her voice was even more shrill than it had been when our brothers fought. They had heard all of this; they were sure it was true. But I was there. I saw the great change in my sister. My sister, as she prepared to leave our house, was radiant; her voice was low, direct, deliberate, unstrange.

It was as though she, yes, she, yes she, had become the king and was now ready to manage and arrange, put the world outside our house in order.

4

I went there every day as my brothers fought, so it was not surprising that I was in my uncle's house when he heard that both of them had died.

At first I noticed a servant enter the room and whisper to Creon that he should come outside. But he shook his head. The second time Creon made his hands into fists and let out a cold sigh before brusquely leaving the room. A moment later he returned and ordered Haemon to follow him.

The servant whispered to Eurydice who closed her eyes in shock and pain.

When Creon and Haemon came back all three of them stared at the ground. No one told me what had transpired. It occurred to me that maybe one of my brothers had been injured or captured and I wanted to go and find Antigone. As the silence continued, the atmosphere more ominous, I realized that maybe one of them was dead.

When I made to stand up my aunt firmly told me to remain.

Stay.

I am alone now in the world. Creon is already a shadow, calling out in pain, his mouth contorted, his eyes rolling in his head, his hands scraping the empty air like claws. When he appears he has to be held by a man on either side of him.

The other two in the room that day are dead as well. My sister is dead. My brothers are dead. My father, yes, my father, my f-father, is dead and the woman who was my mother, she too has passed into shade.

I was still in the room when news came that the bodies of my brothers had been carried to the place of burial. Eteocles' men now called on Creon to unite them as their King.

I saw Creon standing up from where he was. No one spoke.

I am sure that no one spoke. Creon's face was tense and drawn. I watched him so closely that I did not even notice my aunt and Haemon leave the room, although they must have. Perhaps Creon gave some indication that he wanted them to leave, but I do not think so. And I am sure I noticed everything else. And no further messengers arrived.

I watched my uncle as he stood against the wall, his hands still in tight fists by his side. I was alone in the room with him.

It was as if what was occurring in the privacy of his own mind was moving towards me as a sound. He was like the man I saw that day when he had finished tormenting the boy, but the sound was much harder now, more fierce, more complete.

I saw that Creon was almost becoming another man, of whom I had seen merely hints that time before. Night was falling where the day had been, or the sun was rising with all of its savage light as the dullness of the dark retreated.

I knew that the next time Creon spoke he would have a different voice; when he walked his movements would be sharper, more exact; when he had thoughts they would be weighed down by a new burden. I saw his jaw harden and his face become determined. But I was not sure what this meant.

And then, in those last moments before he spoke, I saw something hovering over him, something wounded, troubled, unclean. His brow furrowed and his eyes narrowed as I witnessed him trying to resist and then, with a sigh, taking it in, giving into it, so that it was who he was.

And then he went swiftly to the doorway and ordered the followers of Eteocles to come into the room. It was then that Eurydice and Haemon softly returned and sat close to each other.

Creon stood apart. When the followers arrived and knelt and bowed Creon swept their homage aside.

'Let Eteocles be buried with full ceremony. I have heard from him daily and he held the reins of power with wisdom and restraint. But issue an edict that if anyone should try to bury his brother Polyneices they themselves will be punished, they themselves will be buried alive. The body of Polyneices must rot in the sun, be devoured by roving jackals and vultures. No one must touch his body. He has been the treacherous one. And send out men to find his followers, the ones who have not fled, and have them taken here. They will be dealt with one by one.'

Eurydice gasped as Haemon moved towards her. When Haemon caught my eye I sensed his fear.

And I saw something that no one else saw. I saw Creon in all his weakness. I saw that what had entered his spirit was not strength. The gods had not come to give him wisdom, merely the empty sound that hollow wisdom makes. It was clear to me then that the raging battles already going on within him would grow only more intense. I did not know who he would become.

I only knew what I saw.

I saw the fearful bird of night, ominous and ungainly, ready to beat everything with its savage wings and peck with its sharp, ferocious beak.

That is what I saw.

5

They dragged my sister into the presence of the man who was now the King.

Whatever they had done to her when she was captured there was blood on her mouth and down her chin.

When Haemon went to her, his father stood in his way.

'Do not touch her.'

The guards released her. Antigone moved into the centre of the room and stood facing Creon. As she wiped the blood away she became more composed.

'You have been found,' he said. 'They did not let you escape.'

'I did not seek to escape.'

She put her hair in order and then looked around the room.

'You were found burying your brother. And it is against the law.'

'Law. Oh, I have seen your law.'

'Do you deny that you tried to bury your brother Polyneices? Do you know what the punishment is?'

'I do. I have heard.'

'Do you wish to express regret for what you tried to do? Or, as a woman, claim that you cannot be held responsible for this?'

'Regret? No! I had to move against the vultures, your vultures. My brother's body . . . '

Haemon from the corner tried to speak. He hesitated and then stammered out the words: 'This is the woman who will be my wife.'

'If she does not express remorse for what she tried to do,' Creon said, 'she will marry no one. In the silence of where I will send her there will be no weddings.'

'May I intercede?' Eurydice asked.

'You may weave. And that is what she too will do as my edict is enforced.'

He pointed at me.

Antigone sprang forward.

'She had nothing to do with this. She did nothing.' She could not even look at me.

And so I said, 'My sister is unhinged with grief. Do you not see that in her?'

'I see only defiance,' Creon said.

'Look beyond what you see,' said Eurydice, stepping out of the shadows.

By now, there were many people in this room, including the followers of my brother Eteocles. I noticed that Creon was addressing them as much as he was speaking to my sister or my aunt.

'Outside, there are many people who lost their loved ones in the war, a war that was prolonged by Polyneices. There are bodies that cannot even be found; others are unrecognizable. I cannot allow these people who have suffered because of Polyneices' cruelty . . . I cannot ask them to witness . . . '

'I will be his witness,' my sister interrupted. 'Today I saw . . . I saw my brother's body lying alone, and then one ragged vulture descended. I saw that bird dig one foot deep into the softness of my brother's stomach to give itself balance and strength. The bird dug its beak in through his flesh, to tear out his sinew, his muscle. The smell . . . '

'Of course I do not want this. But I have no choice.'

'My uncle, you have a choice. You are now the King. But instead of thunder, we need thought. It was my brother's body . . . '

Creon turned his gaze fully on my sister.

'Yes, I am the King. I am the one who must decide. There is anger against your brother. Listen to the voices in the street. Ask those who gather in the market. I must attend to those voices. As an uncle I feel only sorrow for what I do; as a king I know that I am right. Antigone, you know so little about life . . . '

'Life? How did you come into the world? How will you leave this life of yours? With your friends and followers, with your crowds in the street? Were they there at the beginning? Will they wash you when your life has left you?'

She stood and faced him directly.

'Answer me. Please! No. You will answer to the crowd.'

He moved towards her threateningly.

'You will only answer those who will elevate you here and now.'

'Yes. For once you are correct. I make edicts for a city where we can live here and now. Someone has to make the law.'

'My uncle, if you listen to the unconsidered voices now, when will they speak to you again, what more will they ask for? Will the voices in the marketplace come to rule you? Us?'

'Your father's tongue does not fit in so sweet a mouth. Antigone, it is clear you have been frightened by what you saw.'

'Frightened? I am frightened? Do you think we cannot see *your* fear? All of us, do you not hear what they say?'

'Who did you hear? What do you know?'

'Nothing, only that a bird descended from the upper air to perform a bloody, vicious rite on my dead brother. Nothing, only that I saw that bird with a chunk of raw torn flesh in its beak. Nothing, only you stole that very thing that keeps us from savagery. What we as women do, what Eurydice does, what my sister does . . . you took that from us and gave it to a foul vulture to perform. That is what I know. Your law sets out to wound not just my life and sully my brother's, it wounds all that came before us and all that will outlast us. The law I live by is the oldest law. It is stark and it is clear. It sees right and it sees wrong. And what I saw is wrong. My law, the law, wounds the life of no one. When these men found me I had begun to whisper the old words of comfort and lament, words that belong to a time beyond markets and streets and edicts.'

Creon hunched his shoulders and then stood up straight. His words came with weariness, as if they had been given to him to say.

'I live in the world of now, of action, not of this . . . this appeal to a time that never was and never will be, this . . . this appeal to an idea of law that makes no sense to those of us whose feet stand firmly on the shifting ground of now. I have to make edicts. You have to obey.'

Antigone bowed her head and spoke softly.

'I do not have to obey.'

Creon continued as though she had not spoken.

'I know what must be done. There will be anger, I can tell you, and more than anger, I am sure, if Polyneices's body is not left where it is. I can tell you. He must . . . '

'They are with him now, those fierce and pitiless birds.'

My sister backed away from him, keeping her eyes fixed on him all the time. His followers made way for her as she edged towards the side of the room.

'Uncle, I must go. It is what I must do. I can save my brother alone. But it must be now. Soon the air will thicken. I must move now and alone.'

Then, as all in the room studied her, I glanced at Creon and I saw that his hands were open and helpless by his side.

I looked at Eurydice; we both knew that none of us should speak.

It was what came from their eyes that I remember as Antigone slowly and with a glittering fullness in her gaze took Creon in and looked straight into his soul.

But then, like a sudden wind designed to whip up fire, Haemon shouted at his father.

'You are the one who forced Eteocles to go to war. I heard you. And you are the one who prolonged the war. The dead bodies are your dead. You are not my father; you are not a king. Antigone in a single thought has more wisdom than you.'

'Get him out of the room!' Creon shouted.

In one second, from a man almost ready to pay attention, he had become a figure filled with thunder.

'Get him out of the room!'

'Leave him!' Eurydice said.

The guards looked from Creon to his wife, wondering which of them to obey.

'There is no time.' Antigone spoke to the followers and then to Creon himself. 'I will bury my brother.'

All I wanted then was for Haemon not to have spoken. I was desperate to return to when Creon and my sister's stances were growing softer.

'Take her away,' my uncle said. 'She knows the edict.'

I went to follow but was stopped at the doorway.

We heard my sister's voice crying out and then the voice becoming fainter until we heard no voice at all.

We heard nothing except the sobs of Haemon as he crouched in a corner of the room.

Creon moved to his followers and began to whisper to them.

I watched to see if my aunt would approach Haemon to

comfort him as his sobs became louder, or if she would appeal to her husband, but she did not.

She was motionless, distant. Stone.

6

A night, a day and a night. And then the unearthly silence, and slowly the birdsong and a gathering blueness in the sky.

It struck me then that the gods knew that this would happen and shut their ears during the time the followers of my brother Eteocles and now the King, my uncle, murdered the followers of my brother Polyneices, the ones they could hunt down.

The gods distracted themselves with their godly concerns, but nothing allowed us mortals to shut our ears. We heard the dogs being unleashed and the snarling and barking and the men holding them back until the dogs seemed to be attacking each other.

And then the panicked screams of the prisoners, the bellowing howls of pain, then the words called out, sharp, fierce — appeals for help, for mercy, imploring the gods, shouting out the names of wives and children, until there were words that went beyond words.

And all through this the intermittent noises of command.

A night, a day and a night when the gods did not hear us, and when the very birds and wild animals learned how harmless and tame they were compared to us, us, the ones who walked and spoke and tilled the fields and sailed on the seas.

Yes, wonders are many, yet none more wonderful than man.

My aunt sat with me. We did not touch or seek any solace from each other. Haemon remained in a corner of the room.

No one had called on us yet to join them or be the ones who would have to beg them for mercy.

A night, a day and a night. And then the bodies were taken away.

We waited, my aunt and Haemon and I. There was no reason to speak.

At some point, I presumed, Creon would appear.

I do not know if he supervised the butchery; it is possible that he merely gave the orders and removed himself from the fray. Perhaps he busied himself with his plans. Perhaps he spoke to one of his followers about the future. Or perhaps he slept through much of it.

He must have been tired.

In one of those late afternoons and early twilights, perhaps the second day we were there, or even the third, something came into my mind.

It is strange how close those images that came to me unbidden were to solid things, to substance, to clarity.

Not merely more memorable, but real, present, true.

I remember it as though it happened.

We are travelling by boat towards an empty place. The sea is calm and the water shallow. When he can no longer row Haemon lowers himself into the water and begins to pull the boat by a rope towards the sand. At first I am alone in the boat, but soon I see Eurydice is with me.

For a time she seems with child, but then it is me. I am with child. The sky looms over us, an overhanging version of the calm water.

Through this blueness the boat moves.

Haemon is intent on his work. He does not look behind.

And then Eurydice whispers to me that we should step from the boat.

Small fish scatter in the water and then some larger fish appear, fish with wings. We try to save ourselves, calling out to Haemon to help us, as one of them rises from the water with all its disturbed energy, flapping, flying towards my face with its scaly wings.

This is not a dream. I live in the terror of that still and I hear Eurydice calling out Haemon's name, calling to him, asking where he is.

I am in the boat again. My arms are oars, desperately propelling us to safety. When I see the room I know we have found a haven, but below me, in the water muddied by sand, my sister and my uncle are moving. They are all dark and dead.

I hear my aunt scream and I sit up and I hear her shouting over and over: 'Where is Haemon?' and then running to the door and appealing to the guards and calling out Haemon's name even louder until Creon comes and then one of the guards tells us that Haemon has been seen moving across the landscape to the place where Antigone is being held.

There is some daylight left as we begin to follow, accompanied by the guards and the men who had been with my brother Eteocles and are now with Creon.

As we rush against the fading light I study them for any sign of what they have been doing — flushed faces or flecks of blood — but they look like ordinary men, innocent almost.

To find the place where they have imprisoned my sister, where they have buried her alive, we have to clamber up a hill, grabbing stalks and bushes to keep steady and find a foothold in the dry, unstable earth. When we arrive we are told that the cave which has been sealed so that my sister will die alone and in darkness has been opened, the stones have been loosened so that someone could enter, and then the cave has been closed up again, but more firmly, and from the inside.

'Pull back the stones,' Creon shouts. 'Open the cave now!'

My aunt and I stand back as Creon's voice is less controlled as he roars out more instructions. By the time the first stone has been loosened he is no longer giving orders, he is whimpering.

When some stones are pushed back into the cave I notice men watching my uncle, their glances cold and withering.

Creon begins calling out the name of his son again and again, pleading, imploring.

When enough stones have been removed, accompanied by torches, we walk into the dank stillness of the cave.

At first the silence reassures me. Soon, I think, we will find my sister in some nook and we will lead her gently out of the cave.

Perhaps, I imagine, Haemon has already found her and they are listening, crouched away from the light.

My eyes are almost accustomed to the darkness when my aunt reaches out and tries to turn me to stop me seeing.

But I do see. I see my sister. She is standing with her head bowed to one side. When my aunt tries to stop me looking I shove her away. And as I move closer I see that Antigone is not standing, she is hanging. Her feet are barely off the ground. Her head is bowed because she is dead. She is dangling from the cord of her own dress tied around a protruding rock. Haemon is kneeling below her, rocking back and forth.

When I try to run to hold her, to see if there is still breath in her, I am stopped by one of the men.

And then, howling, Haemon runs at his father who is inside the mouth of the cave. His father steps easily out of the way as if this is a game. When Haemon turns he fumbles with his sword. And then, with a shriek, he rams the sword through his own body.

No one will let me touch my sister. They move Eurydice and me out of the cave. All we can hear are the cries of Creon as he kneels over the body of his son.

And what I see now are the men standing, almost impatiently. They look like men at the market, men doing business, men who deal in coins or gold or weapons, men waiting to be paid or waiting for a deal to be concluded.

When Creon comes out of the cave, linked by two of his followers, Eurydice whispers to him. He shakes his head, tells her no, but her hands grip his arms, and she whispers with more urgency, more insistence, until he draws himself away from her.

And then he speaks: 'All the bodies must be buried, according to our rites. All of them!'

'Does that include . . . ?' one of his followers begins.

'Yes, that includes Polyneices. Take what remains of him to a place of burial.'

My eyes dart to the men standing at the side. They are nudging each other, smiling darkly. They know, as I know, that it has all been for nothing.

My sister has prevailed.

It is almost night. My aunt helps Creon to go down the hill and holds him as we descend towards the palace.

It seems strange that night could fall and trees be in place and that the customary sounds can still be heard.

But it is so. Our world has changed, but the world itself, the place where we live, remains unaware, as if to warn us of its vast unbending power.

Soon, as if to mock us further, this room holds us both again, my aunt and me. There is no blueness now; it is a dark shadowy space. Creon has gone to be with his followers. When Eurydice says she wants water I call for the servants, but she insists that she needs water immediately and asks me to go myself and fetch it for her.

For some moments thus she is alone in that room. In that time she does what she has planned to do.

When I return she is on the floor. Her face is white, her hands are by her sides, the blood is flowing from her neck. She is already dead.

In that second I think to ask Haemon to go quickly to find his father. In that second I have actually forgotten that he has joined the ranks of the dead.

And then I let out a cry and the servants come and soon the room is full.

Creon kneels and holds Eurydice, cupping his hand under her head. And tenderly he lifts her. Although his voice is loud his attempts at certainty fail him. Although he speaks with care each phrase seems to come with slow shock as if such words have been long in hiding and have now appeared to haunt as much as to appease.

'Rats are breathing now, not you. And snakes have their eyes open, but not your eyes. You will not walk again or speak or whisper to me. Eurydice, can you stay with me? Can you stay with me?'

He lays her body down again gently.

'No, my wife, you cannot stay with me. I must call the women so that we can prepare you for the earth.'

He stands up and looks around the room until he catches my eye.

'What did you say? Yes, you! What did you say?'

'I did not speak. I did not . . . '

'You spoke. What did you say?'

'Uncle, I did not . . . '

'I demand to know what you . . . '

'I did not . . . '

'I will have you taken away if you do not repeat the words you spoke. Mocking me. And I will not tolerate you mocking me.'

From somewhere unearthly, a place where spirits linger, a voice emerges and enters my own voice.

'I am not afraid of you.'

What I whisper does not come from me although it is mine, yes, it is fully mine, as my voice gains in strength.

'I am not afraid of you!'

Creon moves backwards with his hands on his neck.

'I am not afraid of you!'

His fingers are tearing into his own skin.

'I am not afraid of you!'

I wait for some of his men to come for me, but they do not. I remain alone in the centre of the room. When I turn people stand out of my way and, as I leave the palace and walk towards this house, no one seeks to detain me. People who have gathered go indoors when they see me approach.

And through the empty streets I walk with the words coming now like handfuls of clay dug up and thrown aside and more handfuls of clay and more and more.

'I am not afraid of you. Not. Afray. You. I. Afray. No, I. Not. I am. I am. You. Afray. Not afraid. I. Not. You. I not you. I. You. I. I am not afraid of you.'

7

In the hour before dawn my sister comes into this room.

Hunted, wounded, she shivers. Her movements slow and furtive.

There is not a sound.

She turns, her eyes like words . . .

Walk towards the palace and stand in the sunlight.
Accuse them with your silence.
Stand and accuse.
Stare at them!
Standing will be enough. Do not move!
Just stand. Stand!
They will be alone with their fear. How afraid they are by day as much as by night, how they flinch at the smallest sound!
They fear silence more than sound. They are the ones who rule, who have built new palaces in stone, palaces filled with treasure.

In the streets, even by day, no one makes a sound. We live in a time of silence.

There is nothing.

Stand and gaze, that is all I ask, sister, pale sister!

I lift the lamp towards her and I light her with its rays.

She sees me.

Here. She is here. We are here.

When I hold her hand my fingers become hers, her voice

becomes my voice.

The waves on a calm day make only a faint and comforting sound.

A sound that lasts as long as time.

When we fade, so will the truth.

Afraid. She is not afraid . . . I am not afraid . . . My sister . . . You . . . I am not afraid . . . I am not afraid.

Not afraid.

Author's Note

In the spring of 2018, with the actress Lisa Dwan, I co-taught a class at Columbia University called 'The Antigone Project'. We selected fifteen students from many departments in the university; our teaching assistant Carina de Klerk was a graduate student in Classics. This meant that she could take us through the original text of *Antigone* by Sophocles, but also help us with the context. We invited a number of scholars at Columbia — from Law, Classics, Gender Studies, English and Comparative Literature — to address the class. The German filmmaker Volker Schlöndorff, whose version of 'Antigone' forms part of the collaborative film *Germany in Autumn,* and the writer Fintan O'Toole also came to speak to the class.

Over fourteen weeks we analyzed many versions and translations of the play, including two Irish ones by Tom Paulin and Seamus Heaney, others written during the Second World War and in its aftermath by Jean Anouilh and Berthold Brecht, and versions with more contemporary concerns by Athol Fugard, Slajov Zizek, Anne Carson and Kamila Shamsie.

As part of the seminar I began work on my own version of the play; new scenes, as they were created, were presented to students every week. For this, Lisa Dwan and I worked closely together. As soon as a scene was written I would email it to her. She would record it and return it by Dropbox. Then we would begin an intense discussion about the scene, often by phone, sometimes face-to-face. This focussed sometimes on small details in the language and tone, but more often it dealt with broader and more central questions about the figure of Antigone and the position she takes in the play and the character of Creon and how he is seen by an audience.

As Antigone and Creon argued in the text I was writing, Lisa and I discussed the text itself in ways that were often spirited and intense, always civil and invigorating. They pushed me towards writing a more taut and truthful drama.

Both Lisa and I were aware of what was being revealed in the world around us, not least in the theatre and the academy, about gender and power, about abuse of power by men, about silence and speech. Both of us saw how much this play mattered in that debate. Lisa Dwan caused me to see this more sharply and coherently than I did when we started.

The students, each Monday morning, also had strong views on the role of a drama like this as an intervention in the contemporary debate. A few times they came up with brilliant solutions to technical and narrative problems. As each of them set to work on their own projects that related to Antigone I learned a great deal about the power of this text, what it can mean to an audience now and what it meant to audiences in the past.

⌒

I first came across the story of Antigone and Ismene when I was in my late teens. I found it in Conor Cruise O'Brien's *States of Ireland*, published in 1972, in which he quoted in full an article he had written for *The Listener* in October 1968. In this piece he listed the deaths that had resulted from the conflict between Antigone and Creon and commented: 'A stiff price for that handful of dust on Polyneices.' He went on: 'Ismene, who was Polyneices' sister just as Antigone was, would not risk her life for the sake of her brother's dead body.'

O'Brien connected the tensions between authority and the individual in the play with conflicts unfolding in many societies in the real world, including Northern Ireland. 'Creon and Antigone,' he wrote, 'are still part of our nature, inaccessible to advice, and incapable of living at peace in the city.' Antigone, in O'Brien's interpretation of the story, 'is an ethical and religious force, an uncompromising element in our being, as dangerous in her way as Creon, whom she perpetually challenges and provokes'. In a commentary on his 1968 article, written when a hundred people had died in

Northern Ireland (by the time *States of Ireland* went to press that had risen, he added in a footnote, to 'over four hundred and sixty'), O'Brien wrote: 'You begin to feel that Ismene's commonsense and feeling for the living may make the more needful, if less spectacular element in "human dignity".'

At the centre of *Antigone* is a debate about law. Creon is the rightful king and thus he requires that his edicts be assented to. But Antigone appeals to a higher idea of law. In my novel *The Heather Blazing* (1992), the story of a High Court judge in Ireland in the 1980s, I sought to deal with this question of what law is, and what is natural justice, and what would happen if the two notions of law clashed. As the judge in the novel has to work out the balance between two concepts, he sits up late in his study: 'He took a biro from a drawer and began to make squiggles on a pad of paper. What was there beyond the law? "Law"; he wrote the word. There was natural justice. He wrote the two words down and put a question mark after them. And beyond that again there was the notion of right and wrong, the two principles which governed everything and came from God. "Right and wrong"; he wrote the two words down and then put brackets around them and the word "GOD" in capitals beside them.'

The novel form itself seemed ideal to explore what Seamus Heaney called a 'timid circumspect involvement' in public affairs. In the novel that came after *The Heather Blazing, The Story of the Night* (1996), I sought to dramatize the life of a young man in Buenos Aires in the late 1970s and 1980s who lived as though the disappearances were not happening. He noticed nothing and, when it became clear what had actually occurred, he saw no reason why he should think too much about it.

As I spent time in Buenos Aires from 1985 onwards, the Antigone figures — Las Madres de la Plaza de Mayo — dominated the public imagination. They were the conscience of their country. They put themselves in great danger; they appealed to a sense of law and human rights higher than mere legislation or the rule of mere civil authority. Part of their mission was to find the bodies of their loved ones who had disappeared. Their determination gave them their power, but their power also came from the silence that reigned all around them, the numbers who were stirred to do nothing in Argentina in those years.

As I planned *The Story of the Night* I became fascinated by the ambiguous and shadowy position of those who did not follow Antigone's example in Argentina. The more I spoke to those who remained silent, the more I saw how the mixture of timidity, fear and prudence in them was neither stone nor living stream. It could be admitted and then denied; it could be justified and then explained away. It seemed like something that would make more sense in dreams than in waking-time. It could not be pinned down. Thus it was ideal material for a novel.

My interest in writing *Pale Sister* was to explore areas in public life and private conscience that remain indistinct. When I started the play, when Lisa Dwan and I began to work out its moral and political contours, I did not know what Ismene would do. I merely knew she would speak. In the other versions she had been mainly silent. Once she broke that silence some power would have to be released. That was all I knew.

Colm Tóibín